Published by Covenant Communications, Inc. American Fork, Utah

Printed in China
First Printing: October 2009

15 14 13 12 11 10 09   10 9 8 7 6 5 4 3 2 1

ISBN-10 1-59811-876-5
ISBN-13 978-1-59811-876-6

Val Chadwick Bagley

Can you find these pictures in this book?

BONUS FIND

Lehi and the Liahona

Can you find these things?

PLUS:
11 Looking Lizards
9 Goofy Goats

Nephi is commanded to build a ship

Can you find these things?

PLUS:
8 more Smiling Starfish,
8 Crabby Crabs
16 Mischievous Monkeys

BONUS FIND

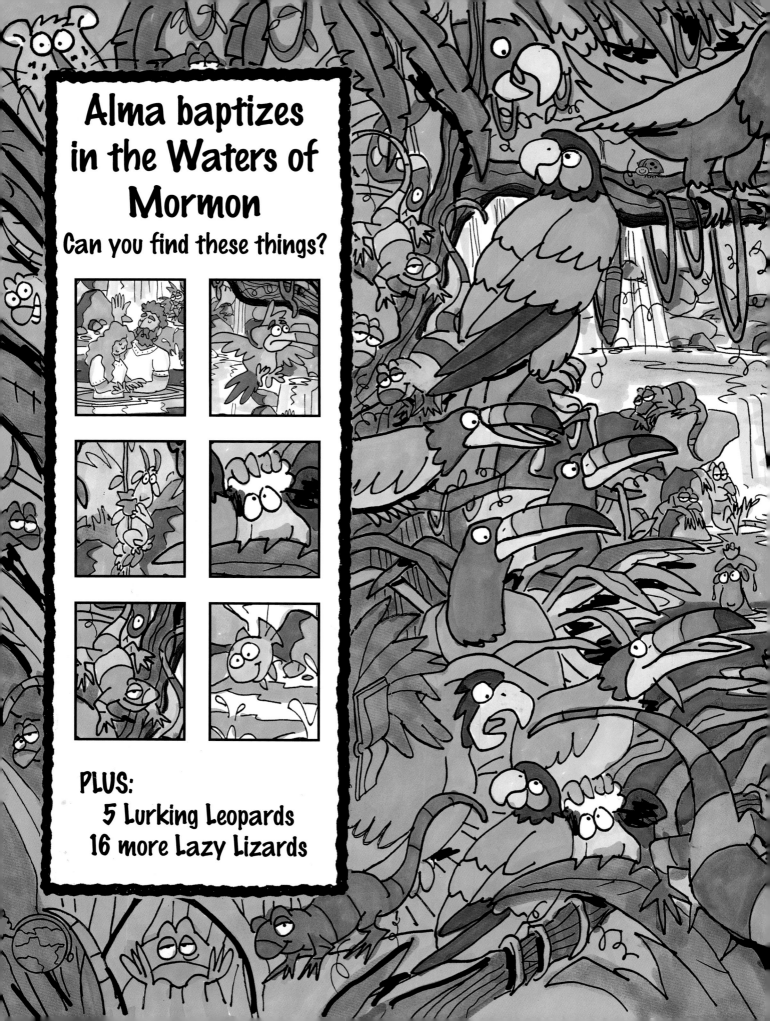

BONUS FIND

BONUS FIND

BONUS
·FIND·

Hagoth, an exceedingly curious man

Can you find these things?

PLUS:
8 more Seasick Seagulls
9 Soaring Seagulls

BONUS
· FIND ·

Jesus visits the people of Nephi

Can you find these things?

PLUS:
4 more Boys from Bountiful
9 more Beautiful Butterflies

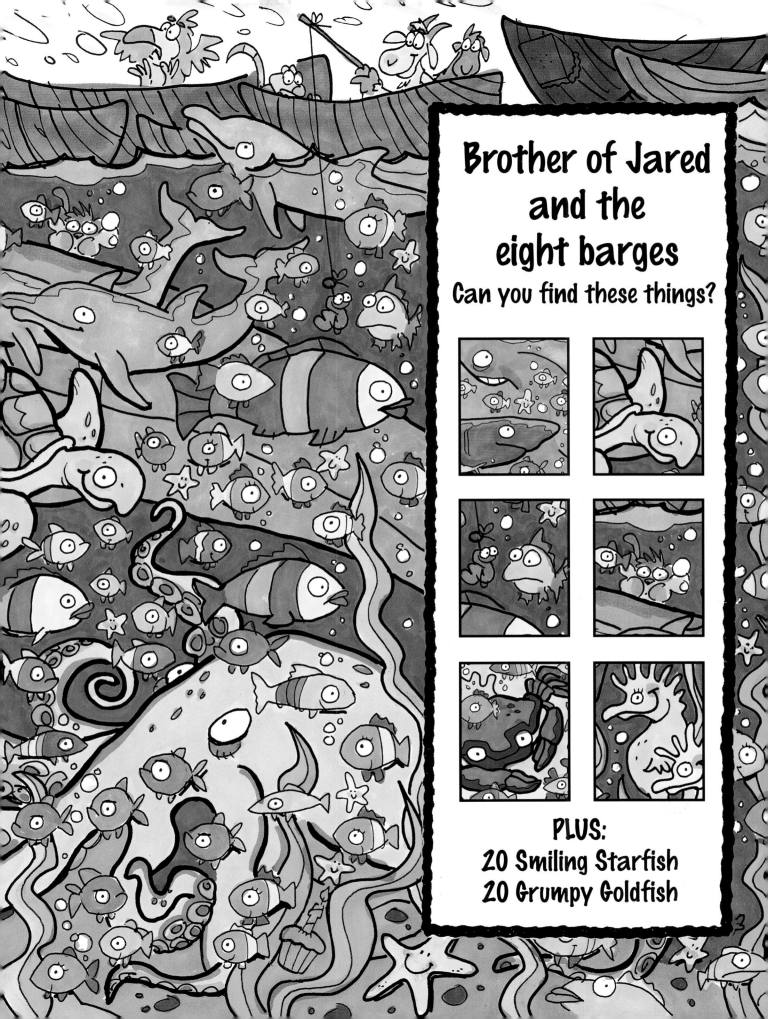

Brother of Jared and the eight barges

Can you find these things?

PLUS:
20 Smiling Starfish
20 Grumpy Goldfish

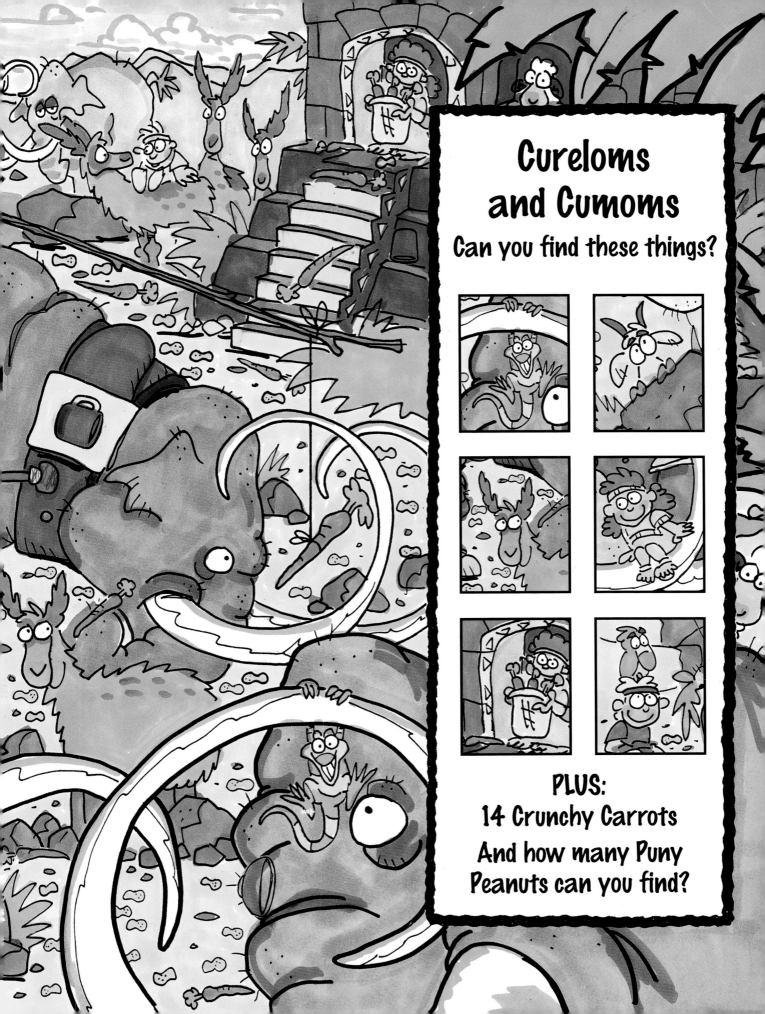

BONUS FIND

Moroni Buries the Golden Plates

Can you find these things?

PLUS:
6 more Squirrelly Squirrels
10 more Funny Bunnies